# Poems From Gtr Manchester

Edited by Donna Samworth

First published in Great Britain in 2007 by:
Young Writers
Remus House
Coltsfoot Drive
Peterborough
PE2 9JX
Telephone: 01733 890066
Website: www.youngwriters.co.uk



SB ISBN 978-1 84602 976 9

# Foreword

Young Writers was established in 1991 and has been passionately devoted to the promotion of reading and writing in children and young adults ever since. The quest continues today. Young Writers remains as committed to the nurturing of poetic and literary talent as ever.

This year's Young Writers competition has proven as vibrant and dynamic as ever and we are delighted to present a showcase of the best poetry from across the UK and in some cases overseas. Each poem has been selected from a wealth of *Little Laureates* entries before ultimately being published in this, our sixteenth primary school poetry series.

Once again, we have been supremely impressed by the overall quality of the entries we have received. The imagination, energy and creativity which has gone into each young writer's entry made choosing the poems a challenging and often difficult but ultimately hugely rewarding task - the general high standard of the work submitted ensured this opportunity to bring their poetry to a larger appreciative audience.

We sincerely hope you are pleased with this final collection and that you will enjoy *Little Laureates Poems From Gtr Manchester* for many years to come.

# Contents

The Poems

## My Pet Pip

I used to have a dog,
The precious, pouncing Pip,
He has died now.
He ran like the wind,
His coat of fur
Glistened in the darkness.
His eyes were like crystals
So shiny and sweet
And the colour of chocolate-brown.
So that was my pet Pip.

**Megan Bailey (8)**
**Aspinal Primary School**

## My Dog

Dylan the Dalmatian dog jumps
About like a bouncing ball.
He chews his juicy bone
And licks the saliva
From his sweaty nose.

**James Loughman (8)**
**Aspinal Primary School**

## My Fish

My fish is like a star,
Shining in the night.

My fish blows bubbles for fun,
She sticks out her yellow tum.

My fish is small,
Like a tiny gem.

**Lucy Galley (9)**
**Aspinal Primary School**

## Favourite Things

I like the taste of chocolate,
Because it's creamy and it melts in my mouth.

I like the smell of my mum's perfume,
Because it smells very fresh and lovely.

I like the feel of my horse's fur coat,
Because it is very soft and warm.

I like the sound of birds singing,
Because it's very peaceful.

I like the look of my two cats, sleeping side by side,
Because it makes me very happy.

**Hollie-Jo Myers (9)**
**Aspinal Primary School**

## My Favourite Things Poem

I like the taste of chocolate,
Melting in my mouth, creamy and soft.

I like the smell of cake,
Making me hungry and wanting to eat.

I like the feel of fur,
So soft and silky.

I like the sound of birds,
Twittering in the trees.

I like the look of a rainbow,
So colourful and bright.

**Alisha Edwards (9)**
**Aspinal Primary School**

## Favourite Things

I like the taste of pasta,
Like curly, wet worms.

I like the smell of doughnuts,
Fresh and sweet.

I like the feel of rabbits,
That are silky and soft.

I like the sound of bike bells,
Ringing in the breeze.

I like the look of the moon,
Shimmering in the light.

**Kayti Dreher (9)**
**Aspinal Primary School**

## Favourite Things

I like the taste of chocolate,
Melting in my mouth.

I like the smell of flowers,
Sweet like lavender.

I like the feel of fur,
So soft like babies' skin.

I like the sound of birds,
Singing in the sky.

**Rebecca Greggan (9)**
**Aspinal Primary School**

## Tigger

Tigger is my pet,
She likes to get wet,
Comes out shimmering
And glimmering,
Like a moon that is bright -
But hides out of sight.

**Luke Brooks (8)**
**Aspinal Primary School**

## Favourite Things

I like the taste of fruit,
Because it's like juice in my mouth.
I like the smell of flowers,
They are very nice.
I like to feel relaxed,
Because it is cool.
I like the sound of a bird,
Because it sings beautifully.

**Hmza Al-Aziz Saadeh (9)**
**Aspinal Primary School**

## Favourite Things

I like the taste of ice cream,
Melting down my throat.

I like the smell of snow bells,
Because they smell sweet.

I like the feel of fur,
All smooth and soft.

I like the sound of trees,
Swinging in the breeze.

I like the look of stars,
Shining in the moonlight.

**Lauren Smith (8)**
**Aspinal Primary School**

## My Pet Dog Snowy

Soft, smooth Snowy,
Was very glowy.
Her bark was beautiful,
And she slept soundly,
Like a baby kitten.
Her eyes were shiny blue,
They shimmered like the moon,
She loved to play
Every day
And that was my dog Snowy.

**Hannah Mooney (8)**
**Aspinal Primary School**

## Favourite Things

I like the taste of chocolate,
So creamy in my mouth.

I like the smell of flowers,
So colourful and bright.

I like the feel of wool,
Like a cloud in the sky.

I like the sound of birds twittering,
So peaceful and calm.

I like the look of my birthday cake,
Dazzling in the light of candles.

**Paisleigh Carr (9)**
**Aspinal Primary School**

## Favourite Things

I like the taste of spaghetti,
Because it wiggles in my mouth.

I like the smell of flowers,
Because they smell fresh.

I like the feel of silk,
It's like my hair, soft and smooth.

I like the sound of my violin teacher,
Because she plays the violin beautifully.

**Emma Darby (8)**
**Aspinal Primary School**

## Rainforest

Raging reds, glowing golds are flames upon a prowling tiger
Scowling, hunting through the dense forest
Where crimson plants sway
Fragile butterflies flutter
Delicate doves glisten
In the shining sunset once told to be incendio.

Water runs in the stream where the tiger stoops
To lap at the ice cool pool
Rippling as torrential rain
Hurls, whirls
Amongst a powerful storm
Beginning as a calm puff of air
Beating, meeting dry earth.

Peace
As soft as silk, the wind brushes
A dripping leaf
Sweeps gently to the ground
With a breeze
And tiger melts away into silent sleep.

**Heather Tyldesley (10)**
**Astley St Stephen's CE School**

## Fire, Water, Air And Earth

Fire is a royal red butterfly
Gliding gently amongst crimson flowers
Beauty beyond description
In the perfumed air
Lives briefly, flickers then dies.

Water is a crystal clear river
Flowing forcefully through golden earth
A twisting journey
In a rich land
Flowing forever to the sea.

Earth is a giant tree of life
Twisting powerfully towards blue sky
A place of growth
Thick with new leaves
Kindly giving new life.

Air is a soft gentle breeze
Floating carelessly through white clouds
Silent and unseen
A single breath
Rising above the earth.

**Beth Ayres (10)**
**Astley St Stephen's CE School**

## River

Gushing, rushing
splishing, splashing
trickling, tapping
swaying, swirling
gliding, gleaming
flowing forward
bashing, bubbling
dripping, drumming
rippling, rolling river.

**Emily Gregory (9)**
**Astley St Stephen's CE School**

## Jungle

Fire is a dazzling orange tiger
dodging from tree to tree
hunting his prey

Wind is a cooling white breeze
swaying from leaf to leaf
like a bird's song

Water is a flowing blue river
twisting from fish to fish
a thirsty animal's drink

Earth is living brown mud
changing from day to day
where creatures live.

**Katie Aspill (9)**
**Astley St Stephen's CE School**

## Fireworks

Fizzing like soda
Jumping like a frog
Whizzing like a windmill
Swooping like a bat
Whirling like a spinning top
Screaming like a ghost
Glittering ice stars
Crashing like waves
Smoke floating like clouds
Creeping like a spy
Drifting like mist.

**Luke Getty (9)**
**Astley St Stephen's CE School**

## Waterfall

Thrusting
running
rushing
leaping
pouring
curling
whirling
splashing
pounding
crashing
floundering
spinning
dripping
waterfall.

**Lucy Roberts (10)**
**Astley St Stephen's CE School**

## Volcano Fire

If I were fire
I'd be a flaming, raging volcano
Red-hot
Crashing like falling rocks
Exploding like a bomb
Fast as the speed of light
Gigantic and tall
Like a leopard speeding through the forest
Pouncing
Like a steady, rumbling drumbeat
I would fear nothing
No one would stand in my way
Strong, powerful
If I were fire.

**Christopher Walsh (9)**
**Astley St Stephen's CE School**

## Fire

Fire is a dazzling scarlet dragon
Flipping and flying through the still air
Roaring his raging red flames
In a burst of temper
Exploding his anger
Flickering his golden tongue
Shouting
Until calm
His anger turns to ashes
Whirling black flakes to earth.

**Jordan Guest (9)**
**Astley St Stephen's CE School**

## Jungle Journey

Slowly, stealthily
The tiger creeps through the dense jungle
Glowing, golden
A luminous orange coat of flame
Raging red eyes
A roar that echoes
Breaking silence
Travelling to the river
That ripples and trickles
Through the forest leaves
A drink for survival
Life
Blown by the breeze
That whistles and whines
Sends a leaf spinning
Across the secure
Life-giving earth.

**Ben Gregory (10)**
**Astley St Stephen's CE School**

## Tiger

A scarlet-red tiger is fire
Prowling through the sunlit jungle,

By river water that trickles and splashes
Through rain falling on leaves

Which grow on earth root trees
Silent with no one to disturb them.

Blown by a breeze, a mystery
Which can grow strong enough to tear down the tree.

**Jordan Hughes (8)**
**Astley St Stephen's CE School**

## The Jungle

A fiery golden panther prowls
through the jungle to the cool blue river.
Stripes glisten in the glowing sunset
as it drinks where the water
ripples and rides.

A slender snake slithers
through riverbank leaves, hunting.
His earth-black eyes fixed
on a tree-brown rat scurrying by.

A gust of wind ruffles his fur,
makes a leaf dance.
The snake slithers and slides
as the wind twists and turns
under the dashing, dazzling jungle sun.

**Jeni Newton (10)**
**Astley St Stephen's CE School**

# If . . .

If I were Earth
I'd be an ancient tree watching each creature grow,
I'd feel like the leader of the forest tribe,
I'd sound like an owl's hoot in the still depths of night,
I'd look like a muddy skyscraper,
I'd move like an old man, unsteady and swaying,
I'd be like the cat that prowls alone at night,
I'd sound like the creaking of a door,
I'd fear the human-destroying woodcutter,
I'd want respect,
I'd feel strong.

**Hannah Brown (10)**
**Astley St Stephen's CE School**

## The Glorious Rainforest

The rainforest sees,
The glorious colours of exotic birds, resting in the trees.

The rainforest hears,
The sound of whispers in the breeze.

The rainforest sees,
The change of the chameleons' colours day after day.

The rainforest hears
The rustle of damp, clammy leaves.

The rainforest sees,
Animals enjoying their freedom.

**Louise Warr (10)**
**Cams Lane CP School**

## The Revolting Castle

The castle hears -
The starving screams of the prisoners.

The castle sees -
Loyal people banqueting.

The castle hears -
The soldiers marching gracefully down the winding corridors.

The castle sees -
Heartbroken, sorrowful prisoners, whimpering for food.

The castle hears -
The crashes of the mouldy moat.

The castle sees -
The long-lost princess in the highest tower.

**Shannon Bannister (11)**
**Cams Lane CP School**

## Laughter In Heaven

The beach sees -
Breaking and crashing waves, hammering the chalky cliffs.

The beach hears -
The slosh and splatter of stones, skimming the surface of the waves.

The beach sees -
Mothers slapping sun lotion onto their squirming children.

The beach hears -
The distant sound of cruise ships, blowing out steam as they roll
into the sunset.

The beach sees -
The bewildered faces of children exploring the rugged rocks,
crouching, waiting, wondering.

The beach hears -
Rapturous laughter, spreading across the landscape like
a deadly virus.

**Jenna Haslam (11)**
**Cams Lane CP School**

## The Ice Palace

The Arctic hears -
Enthusiastic Eskimos, talking through a serious snowstorm.

The Arctic sees -
Puzzled polar bears, plodding towards the whirling water.

The Arctic hears -
Whipping winds howling, deafening all the wonderful wildlife.

The Arctic sees -
Spectacular snow softly, silently falling onto the ice.

The Arctic hears -
Walruses splash and splosh, to and fro, to the shimmering sea.

The Arctic sees -
Perky penguins slowly shuffling together, to keep their extraordinary
eggs warm.

**Eleanor Fryett (11)**
**Cams Lane CP School**

## The Hot And Humid Jungle

The jungle sees -
The beautiful bright colours of the macaws, squawking and
squeaking in the palm trees.

The jungle hears -
The growling of the tigers, pouncing and prowling through the vines.

The jungle sees -
The smooth shining skin of the tree frog, glowing and gleaming
in the sunlight.

The jungle hears -
The splash and snap of the ravenous piranhas, leaping out of the
fast gushing water.

The jungle sees -
The bright yellow eyes of the crocodile, watching and waiting.

The jungle hears -
The irritating buzz of the mosquitoes, hovering and darting through
The hot and humid jungle.

**Leah Wakefield (11)**
**Cams Lane CP School**

## Through The Jungle

The jungle sees -
Leaping leopards, lying in wait.

The jungle hears -
Cheeky crocodiles, creeping in wild water.

The jungle sees -
Slithering snakes, spinning over smooth ground.

The jungle hears -
Hummingbirds hovering over high trees.

The jungle sees -
Tough tigers tracking down its prey.

The jungle hears -
Proud parrots, pecking on their food.

**Kirsty Brand (10)**
**Cams Lane CP School**

## Searching

I can find an idea . . .
Nestled next to a cold, immense igloo.

Crouched behind a crumbling, individual iceberg.

Surfing on top of a powerful, streamlined penguin.

Resting amongst a scanty seal's snout.

Watching over endangered precious polar bears.

Admiring various adjacent views.

**Claire Fuller (10)**
**Cams Lane CP School**

## What Does A Castle Do?

The castle hears -
Clashes of cold metal from the scary suit of armour.

The castle sees -
Suffering, heartbroken ghosts of past prisoners.

The castle hears -
Weeping from many mourners, who mourn miserably
For brave people who have lost their light-hearted lives in battle.

The castle sees -
Worrying, winding corridors that unfortunately never end.

The castle hears -
Many magnificent tunes played perfectly on a piano.

The castle sees -
Itself, cloaked in cold mist.

**Emily Bradbury (11)**
**Cams Lane CP School**

## Scary

The haunted house hears -
The creaking of doors opening and closing.

The haunted house sees -
An old rusty chest, locked with a code that's unknown.

The haunted house hears -
Banging of old pictures falling from burnt walls.

The haunted house sees -
Ripped curtains blowing frantically through the deserted windows.

The haunted house hears -
Wood creaking as spirits walk across their rooms.

The haunted house sees -
Remnants of rough rope, hanging from the ceiling.

**Emma Nicholson (10)**
**Cams Lane CP School**

## The Raging City

The city hears -
Livid drivers beeping their horns, as they drive
dangerously down the road.

The city sees -
Weary teenagers, sitting listlessly.

The city sees -
Gigantic skyscrapers grabbing for the sky.

The city hears -
Frantic planes, flying through the sky.

The city sees -
Alarmed people escaping the buildings.

**Lucy Gale (11)**
**Cams Lane CP School**

## Exploring The Ocean

The ocean sees -
Seething sharks, swimming for their perplexed prey.

The ocean hears -
Delighted dolphins, squeaking cheerfully.

The ocean sees -
Friendly fish softly swaying in the crystal-clear sea.

The ocean hears -
The light-hearted sea, heaving while it is sparkling.

The ocean sees -
Spume, shimmering in the sapphire-blue sea.

The ocean hears -
The estuary euphorically combine.

**Aisha Ali (11)**
**Cams Lane CP School**

## The Gruesome House

The haunted house sees -
The bloodthirsty zombies creeping around.

The haunted house hears -
The slurping zombies, quenching the boys' blood.

The haunted house sees -
Owls, swooping around, snatching anything in their paths.

The haunted house hears -
The ghouls, rattling all the chairs.

The haunted house sees -
Spooked spinsters, scuttling for cover.

The haunted house hears -
The bogeyman, banging bleakly through the house.

**Simon Rogers (10)**
**Cams Lane CP School**

## Where Can I Find An Idea?

I can find an idea -
Hiding behind a grim, gruesome graveyard,
Scuttling around the dark silky spider,
Hung above the cracked skeleton head,
Nestled next to the mouldy, deadly tree,
Waiting under the white skeleton bones,
Munching near the deadly tree,
Frightened over the black rusty gate,
Where can you find an idea?

**Shiraz Mahmood (11)**
**Cams Lane CP School**

## The Amazing Jungle

The jungle hears -
The snakes hiss on the jungle ground.

The jungle sees -
The vivid wonderful, unexplored flowers.

The jungle hears -
The gorilla beating his colossal chest.

The jungle sees -
The cheeky monkeys jumping from tree to tree.

The jungle hears -
The amazing noise of the birds of paradise.

The jungle sees -
The high, huge tree house.

**Daniel Danson (11)**
**Cams Lane CP School**

## Where Can I Find An Idea?

I can find an idea -
Located in the fabulous football stadium,
Lurking near the gleaming goalpost,
Nestled beside the bright blue seats,
Lunging into a leg-breaking tackle,
Crouched under the marvellous manager's dugout,
Glancing towards the other end of the pitch,
Waiting along the sideline,
Looking above the super stadium.
Where can you find an idea?

**Jack Berry (11)**
**Cams Lane CP School**

## Mountain Mayhem

The mountain hears -
The shrill of the yodeller's voice.

The mountain sees -
The gorgeous view below.

The mountain hears -
The laughter of heroic climbers.

The mountain sees -
A baffled, gormless mountain goat.

The mountain hears -
The ruthless rocks penetrating anything in their path.

The mountain sees -
Sneaky snow leopards devouring their prey.

**Jordyn Fitton (11)**
**Cams Lane CP School**

## Haunted House

The haunted house hears -
Frightened mice from creaky doors.

The haunted house sees -
Frightened cats in the pitch-black.

The haunted house hears -
Knights charging at their mean enemies.

The haunted house sees -
Dead antelope heads and black horns.

The haunted house hears -
Smashing bulbs and lights from old cables.

The haunted house sees -
Winding passages full of secret doors.

**Levi Benjamin (11)**
**Cams Lane CP School**

## The City

The city sees -
A strange stray cat, clawing a cookie.

The city hears -
Rip-roaring engines, racing down the road.

The city sees -
Rats, rooting through the rubbish.

The city hears -
A dustbin clattering to the floor.

The city sees -
A poor beggar, praying for money.

The city hears -
The crack of smashing windows.

**Jake Dighton (11)**
**Cams Lane CP School**

## The Hell House

The haunted house sees -
Ghosts, floating through the black of night.

The haunted house hears -
The wails of the supernatural ghouls.

The haunted house sees -
The monsters, preying on innocent people.

The haunted house hears -
The creaks of the old crooked stairways.

The haunted house sees -
The blood, slithering down the damp door.

The haunted house sees -
The deadly screams from the banshee.

**Harrison Manders (11)**
**Cams Lane CP School**

## The Gloomy, Ghostly House

The haunted house can see -
Dark beings killing, startling, scaring people at the stroke of midnight.

The haunted house can hear -
Silence digging into all alive creatures.

The haunted house can see -
The spider webs shake, shimmer, shine in the flickering lights.

The haunted house can hear -
Rattling, creaking, hammering of beings, sealing the fate of
their victims.

The haunted house can see -
The blue blood of monstrous monsters.

The haunted house can hear -
Black, brutal and bloodsucking bats, flying fearfully about.

The haunted house can see -
Knights swiping their swords upon helpless humans.

The haunted house can hear -
Creaking doors being locked by ghoulish, gruesome ghostly hands.

**Callum Lewis (11)**
**Cams Lane CP School**

## Where Can I Find An Idea?

I can find an idea -
Spinning up in space.
Zooming around the solid, rough asteroids.
Hovering over pointless, peaceful planets.
Stumbling between huge bright stars.
Standing on the grey empty moon.
Huddling inside the small cramped space shuttle.
Hiding behind the heat of the boiling sun in space.

**Kurtis Gould (10)**
**Cams Lane CP School**

## Where Can I Find An Idea?

I can find an idea -
Curled in the referee's whistle,
Lingering low on the pitch,
Nestled next to the pristine crossbar,
Cowering in front of the footballers,
Hurled menacingly through the air by frustrated fans,
Running rapidly outside the changing rooms,
Blasted against a flying football,
Overlooking the match in the commentary box.
All in a football stadium.

**Jack Owens (11)**
**Cams Lane CP School**

## The Clammy, Cold Mountain

The mountain sees -
Hikers walking up the rough, rugged, snowy path.

The mountain hears -
The anxious eagles flying in the air.

The mountain sees -
Snow leopards springing off the slippery snow.

The mountain hears -
Screaming snowboarders as they furiously slide down the
smooth, cold snow.

The mountain sees -
Climbers struggling to climb the crumbling mountain face.

The mountain hears -
The ptarmigan chirping away in the frosty snow.

**Jack Drakley (11)**
**Cams Lane CP School**

## Swap? Sell? - Small Ads Sell Fast

Brother, 1988 model
Mean ride, has not passed MOT
Needs a lot doing to him
Reaches top speed 100mph
(no faster, otherwise will break down)
Stalls a lot
Radio does not work
Code lost
Engine not so good
Owner hates him
Because argues all the time.

Will swap for anything.

**Christian Boyd**
**Our Lady of the Rosary RC Primary School**

## Swap? Sell? - Small Ads Sell Fast

1992 brother,
Plays CDs and DVDs,
Shiny clean colour,
Runs on noodles and juice,
And also a bit of chocolate mousse,
Top speed - 228mph,
And nice fast ride,
Will trade for something well equipped.

1996 cousin,
Very annoying,
Volume/voice 10,000 decibels at highest,
Runs on cheese from the kitchen,
Top speed 199mph,
Will trade for a Ford,
Less annoying with a quieter radio.

**Keenan Doherty (11)**
**Our Lady of the Rosary RC Primary School**

## Swap? Sell? - Small Ads Sell Fast

For sale,
1999 sister,
Ex cond often screeches,
Runs on biscuits, crisps and milk,
Rear has a problem,
To be washed weekly.
Price £50 ono or trade for 1997 turbo.

For sale,
1996 friend,
Produces a comfortable ride,
Special edition, long series,
Colour blue,
£150 ono, good condition,
Runs on Diet Coke and digestive biscuits.

**Cameron Baynes (10)**
**Our Lady of the Rosary RC Primary School**

## Swap? Sell? - Small Ads Sell Fast

1996 good friend Hannah, ten years old.
Quiet.
Fast runner.
Needs new engine.
A new coat of paint wouldn't be a bad idea.
Good wheels.
Will take whatever you're prepared to give.
Type: old banger.

1996 great mate Emma, ten years old.
Noisy.
Breaks down in cold weather.
Has a mind of her own and mostly spins out of control.
Repairs needed.
May need spraying to get rid of cheesy smell.
Will take only something in the Ferrari range.
Type: turquoise Beetle.
Beware: may contain fluffy dice.

**Bethany Drum (11)**
**Our Lady of the Rosary RC Primary School**

## Swap? Sell? - Small Ads Sell Fast

1995 friend.
Model, not many like this!
In tip-top condition,
Although he stalls at inconvenient moments.
Reaches top speed.
Sometimes breaks down.
You must stop to view.
Needs a lot of attention and TLC.
Will only swap for £3,000 rrp.

1993 sister.
Doesn't need any respray.
In excellent condition.
Provides a comfortable ride - although sometimes not!
0mph in the morning.
Runs on crisps and petrol.
Will only swap for something quite special.

**Olivia Shaw (11)**
**Our Lady of the Rosary RC Primary School**

## Swap? Sell? - Small Ads Sell Fast

1999 sister.
Good dancer; a prancer dancer,
Beautiful singer but looks like a total minger,
Boasting, reaches top speed and loves her toaster,
Frequently overtaking a show car,
Evil, stalls at inconvenient moments,
Sounds and screams like a horn.

1943 old grandma.
Not many like this,
In such a clean and rust-free state,
Please stop to have a view,
Got MOT a couple of days ago - phew!
Been trying for ages, finally got through!

**Amy McAleer (11)**
**Our Lady of the Rosary RC Primary School**

## Swap? Sell? - Small Ads Sell Fast

2006 cousin.
Good runner, low mileage.
Runs on milk, baby oil.
Does need some attention.
Leaks oil a lot, streamlined spoiler.
Nice rims, not stable at high speeds.
Customised rear end, passed MOT.
Will only swap for something quite special.

1995 Wood model, good pal.
Runs on milk, chocolate and water.
V12 engine, twin turbo carbon fibre hood.
Lots of storage, passed MOT yesterday.
Top speed, 252 miles per hour, special edition.
Will only swap for something special.

**Jack Judge (11)**
**Our Lady of the Rosary RC Primary School**

## Swap? Sell? - Small Ads Sell Fast

1995 friend,
Not many like this,
Runs on Diet Coke and needs a lot of TLC,
But in ex.cond.
Passed MOT last week.
Model a 'Show',
I will sell for anything!
Please!

2003 sister,
Radio in good cond.
But prefers to play CDs,
Needs a lot of attention,
Quite a boaster,
I will only sell for something unique.

**Katie McCabe (11)**
**Our Lady of the Rosary RC Primary School**

## Swap? Sell? - Small Ads Sell Fast

1958 dad, in quite good condition.
Not many like this.
Not too much grey, so won't be hard to spray over.
I exchange for, a top of the range twin turbo engine sports type.
Will only swap if worth it.

1959 mum, a very hard worker.
Twelve miles per gallon.
Hasn't any body repairs
And can cope with most roads.
Will only exchange for something even more brilliant.

**Robert Paradiuk (11)**
**Our Lady of the Rosary RC Primary School**

## Swap? Sell? - Small Ads Sell Fast

1994 sister for sale.
Alright runner.
Has extremely loud radio and uses hydraulics like a dancing hippo.
Top speed 14mph, frequently overtakes but fails.
Plays on 'sat nav' a lot and beeps horn when speaking.
Will trade for samurai sword.

1960 middle-aged uncle for sale.
Smooth runner but has rust on front bumper
Is greasy all the time and has excellent brown coating.
Keeps cigarettes in ashtray and an Xbox hidden on back seat.
Some repairs needed.
Will swap for PlayStation 3.

**Liam Partington (11)**
**Our Lady of the Rosary RC Primary School**

## Swap? Sell? - Small Ads Sell Fast

1998 brother.
As fast as any other.
A few scratches here and there,
Nothing that can't be fixed.
Dangerous weapon at the front.
Been in many crashes but has lived to tell the tale.
Will swap for anything.

1998 sister. Solo.
Doesn't need much attention.
Runs on toast and orange juice.
Not too much to ask.
Needs polishing every now and then.
Would like a younger version in exchange.

**Ella Loynes (11)**
**Our Lady of the Rosary RC Primary School**

## Gorillas

Mine is the beat
That wakes the land
In an African world;
Mine are the paws.

Mine is the meat
That people eat
In an African world;
The heat is on.

Mine are the hands
That hunters trade
Mine are the hands;
I am afraid.

**Jack O'Grady (10)**
**Our Lady of the Rosary RC Primary School**

## Mine Is The Beat

Mine is the beat
That rocks the world
But the hunters take me for meat.
Mine is the beat.

Mine are the paws
That stand on the shores
Of the glistening silver lake.
Mine are the paws.

Mine are the eyes
That look around
But then I have to crouch down.
Mine are the eyes.

**Jacob Lloyd (9)**
**Our Lady of the Rosary RC Primary School**

## Tigers

Mine is the purr
That shakes the trees
On the African plains;
Mine are the paws that wafts the bees.

Mine are the stripes
That hide me just fine
When danger is near;
Mine are the eyes that shine.

Mine is the fur
Made into a coat
Mine is the fur;
My home is remote.

**Sarah Bloor (10)**
**Our Lady of the Rosary RC Primary School**

## Seals

Mine is the whine,
That chills the spine.
In this icy place,
That hides me so fine.

Mine is the skin,
They club me for.
That holds my heart within,
And hurts me to the core.

Mine is the tail,
That slaps on the water.
Mine is the tail,
I am in pain.

**Elizabeth McGrory (10)**
**Our Lady of the Rosary RC Primary School**

## Gorillas

Mine are the paws
That strip the leaves
In the enclosure
Of the massive trees.

Mine are the ears
That listen for fears
I try to run
Now they are near.

Mine are the eyes
Full of sorrow and tears
Mine are the eyes;
The huntsmen gun, the gorilla fears.

**Benjamin Coleman (9)**
**Our Lady of the Rosary RC Primary School**

## Rhinos

Mine is the rumble,
That shakes the land,
On the plains of Asia;
I charge through sand.

Mine are the tusks
My lethal weapons.
When danger is close
I use my weapons.

Mine are the tusks
That are hunted down
Mine are the tusks;
Lost is my ivory crown!

**Thomas Alexander (10)**
**Our Lady of the Rosary RC Primary School**

## Gorillas

Mine are the paws
With a great big thud,
Beating my chest,
As I travel through the mud.

Mine is the cry,
Sensing hunters near,
This is all I have heard,
It is all clear.

Mine is the meat,
I watch in my nest,
Mine is the meat,
That the hunters request.

**Zoe Sweeney (10)**
**Our Lady of the Rosary RC Primary School**

## Tiger

Mine is the call
On the darkest night
In the forest;
Mine is the bite.

Mine is the ear
Listening to you
If he comes near
Run away, do.

Mine is the print
That glows so bright
Mine is the print;
I'm full of fright.

**Abigail Lowe (10)**
**Our Lady of the Rosary RC Primary School**

## Tiger

Mine is the growl
That is known all around
In the grasses of India;
I am barely ever found.

Mine are the canines
That take a savage bite
When danger is close;
Mine is the ghastly fright.

Mine is the fur
The huntsmen trade;
Mine is the fur
I am very afraid.

**Luke McGrory (10)**
**Our Lady of the Rosary RC Primary School**

## Tigers

Mine is the roar
That shakes the land
In an Indian world;
My stripes are grand.

Mine is the ear
That hears the gun
In an Indian world;
I try to run.

Mine are the stripes
That cover me;
Mine are the stripes
I don't feel free.

**Ella May Embleton (10)**
**Our Lady of the Rosary RC Primary School**

## Tigers

Mine is the roar
That fills the air
With sorrow in my heart;
In the darkness of the night.

Mine is the echo
Through the jungle
Which hear the huntsmen shout;
Mine is the ear.

Mine is the fur
I am so scared
Mine is the fur;
I wish the huntsmen cared.

**Kate Mullen (9)**
**Our Lady of the Rosary RC Primary School**

## Tigers

Mine is the growl
That shakes the ground
In the jungle near;
Mine is the sound.

Mine are the claws
Like a lethal dagger
When danger is here;
When I am hurt I stagger.

Mine is the fur
That huntsmen trade
Mine is the fur;
I am afraid.

**Rebecca Hartley (9)**
**Our Lady of the Rosary RC Primary School**

## Elephants

Mine is the thump,
That shakes the land,
In an African world;
Mine is the thump that lifts the sand.

Mine is the voice,
That called my herd,
In an African world;
I am the elephant that is always heard.

Mine are the tusks,
That are hunted down,
Mine are the tusks,
That are worn in town.

**Natasha Jachim (10)**
**Our Lady of the Rosary RC Primary School**

## Elephants

Mine is the thud,
That shakes the land
In an African world;
My tusks are grand.

Mine are the ears,
That listen for fear,
In an African world;
What can I hear?

Mine are the tusks,
The huntsmen trade;
Mine are the tusks
I am afraid.

**Nicole Smith (9)**
**Our Lady of the Rosary RC Primary School**

## Seals

Mine is the yelp
That huntsmen will hear
When that net covers me;
I shed a tear.

Mine is the nose
It's very wet
I smell danger;
I'm not free yet.

Mine is the skin
That is clubbed to death
Mine is the skin
People mean death.

**Sian McManamon (10)**
**Our Lady of the Rosary RC Primary School**

## Orang-Utan

Mine is the yell,
That calls my friend,
In a dark treetop;
I wish it could end.

Mine is the paw,
Orange with fur,
In a dark treetop;
With not one to care.

Mine is the fur,
Killed for fun,
*Bang, bang,* gone;
With a gun.

**Niamh Scully (9)**
**Our Lady of the Rosary RC Primary School**

## Seal

Mine is the skin
That huntsmen crave
In a freezing land;
My skin I need to save.

Mine are the whiskers
That twitch and quiver
As hunters draw near;
My fur shivers.

**Jake Saleh (9)**
**Our Lady of the Rosary RC Primary School**

## Bears

Mine is the roar
That shakes the trees
In the natural world;
Hunters come and I fall to my knees.

**Kerry Shaw (9)**
**Our Lady of the Rosary RC Primary School**

## Seals

Mine is the cry
That charms all,
In this place of ice;
Mine is the call.

Mine is the tail
That swishes and swings,
When danger is close;
My mouth, it sings.

Mine is the skin
The Inuit strip,
Mine is the skin;
My life, they rip.

**Lucy Thomas (9)**
**Our Lady of the Rosary RC Primary School**

## Bears

Mine is the roar
That shakes the trees,
In a forest deep and dark;
Mine is the roar.

**Jack Hume (9)**
**Our Lady of the Rosary RC Primary School**

## Anger

Anger looks like a volcano about to explode.
Anger feels like steam coming out of my ears.
Anger sounds like drums booming down my ears.
Anger tastes like spicy hot chilli peppers.
Anger smells like rotten eggs.

**Liam Timperley (8)**
**St Clare's RC Primary School, Blackley**

## Joy

Joy feels like a summer's day.
Joy looks like flowers floating.
Joy sounds like birds singing.
Joy tastes like soft fish.
Joy smells like honey.

**Lewis Rouse (9)**
**St Clare's RC Primary School, Blackley**

## Joy

Joy looks like a sunny week.
Joy feels like a fast ride.
Joy sounds like people laughing.
Joy tastes like eating an ice cream.
Joy smells like a chocolate bar.

**Hannah Murphy (9)**
**St Clare's RC Primary School, Blackley**

## Sadness

Sadness smells like strong fresh chlorine from a swimming pool.
Sadness sounds like thunder and lightning.
Sadness feels like a smushy and hard smoothie.
Sadness tastes like a one-week-old sweet.
Sadness looks like a baby crying and an animal dying.

**Chantelle Kidd (10)**
**St Clare's RC Primary School, Blackley**

## Anger

Anger looks like a raging man.
It feels like a big fist coming towards me.
It sounds like the Incredible Hulk *raaa!*
It tastes like you could die at any second.
It smells like steam out of someone's ears.

**Keenan Buck (9)**
**St Clare's RC Primary School, Blackley**

## Love

Love feels like a smooth soft hand
waiting to be placed in the sand.

Love looks like two birds
in a tree tweeting words.

Love sounds like a flower
growing with all its might and power.

Love smells like lots of roses
as it stands there and poses.

Love tastes sweet
Just sweet
Juicy, tasteful.
Never wasteful!

**Courtney Miller (10)**
**St Clare's RC Primary School, Blackley**

## Fear

Fear looks like sharp knives hanging on the wall and feels
dead hard and pointy.
Sounds like someone screaming from behind.
Tastes like dripping blood and guts, if you know
what guts taste of.
And fear smells like someone sneaking in the dark.

Fear feels like someone has just punched you in the face.
And smells like fresh death in the air.
It sounds like small bats flying around your head
And tastes like something hot, bubbling in your mouth.
It looks like ten skeletons hanging in the air.

**Lucy Cooke (9)**
**St Clare's RC Primary School, Blackley**

## Love

Love looks like a big red love heart.
Love feels like a big brown cuddly bear.
Love sounds like birds singing on a tree, whistling, 'Yippee'.
Love tastes like hot chocolate, dripping till it has gone.
Love smells like five candy sticks crunching.

**Shannon Barlow (9)**
**St Clare's RC Primary School, Blackley**

## Love

Love feels like a fluffy kitten.
It looks like a lovely flower.
It sounds like a sweet bird singing.
It tastes like lovely cocoa.
It smells like sweet perfume.

It feels like a fluffy cloud.
It looks like a baby bird.
It sounds like the sweet ring of a bell.
It tastes like cake.
It smells like apple juice.

Love feels like somebody's soft clothes.
It looks like a sunny day.
It sounds like somebody singing a song.
It tastes like smooth chocolate.
It smells like Milky Way.

Love feels like sweets.
It looks like a fluffy puppy.
It sounds like soft relaxing music.
It tastes like ice cream.
It smells like sweet jelly.

**Charlotte Johnson (9)**
**St Clare's RC Primary School, Blackley**

## Worried

Worry looks like a question mark
travelling through a worried heart.

Worry feels like a sinking boat,
sinking down a gigantic throat.

Worry sounds like an animal's creep,
just like a mouse's squeak!

Worry tastes like butterflies
looking through some glassy eyes.

Worry smells like a spicy curry
or like a giant foot trying to squash me in a hurry!

**Georgina Wilkinson (10)**
**St Clare's RC Primary School, Blackley**

## Love

Love looks like two people stuck in a giant love heart.
It feels like a happy couple getting married.
It sounds like wedding bells ringing.
Love tastes like a wedding cake.
Love smells like a chocolate bar.

**Olivia Cunningham (9)**
**St Clare's RC Primary School, Blackley**

## Anger

Anger feels like an earthquake rocking in my head.
It sounds like thunder coming from far under.
It tastes like a meatball rolling and rumbling in my mouth.
It smells like a fire burning fiercely below.
It looks like a volcano erupting with hot, horrible lava.

**Laura Saunders (9)**
**St Clare's RC Primary School, Blackley**

## Anger

Anger is like a devil with an aqua trident.
Anger feels like a spike splitting you into two.
Anger sounds like a rumble of thunder.
Anger tastes like sweat and blood.
Anger smells like a rubbish bin.

**Louis McGowan (9)**
**St Clare's RC Primary School, Blackley**

## Love

Love looks like a path for those in love.
Love feels like chocolate melting.
Love sounds like people laughing.
Love tastes like ice cream.
Love smells like roses.

**Alice Dale (10)**
**St Clare's RC Primary School, Blackley**

## Anger

Anger looks like a raging volcano.
Anger feels like a fist about to explode.
Anger sounds like a rhino setting off.
Anger tastes like fire in my mouth.
Anger smells like blazing fire in my heart.

**Jordan Moss (10)**
**St Clare's RC Primary School, Blackley**

## Joy

It looks like a sweet car on fire.
It sounds like a sweet hummingbird.
It feels like melting ice cream.
It smells like hot steam.
It tastes like oil dripping from the pipes.

**Conor Holmes (9)**
**St Clare's RC Primary School, Blackley**

## Anger

Anger feels like walls closing in on you.
It looks like a dull and boring day.
Anger tastes like a bowl of green slimy jelly.
It smells of burning houses.
Anger sounds like screeching blackboards.

**Chelsea Davenport (9)**
**St Clare's RC Primary School, Blackley**

## Smoking Kills

S moking kills!
M ore people smoke than ever before.
O pen your mind to what smoking can do.
K ick the habit or
I n Heaven people can go, so
N o smoking
G ive it up today!

**Emily Moffatt (8)**
**St Clement's CE Primary School, Higher Openshaw**

## Safety

As I look out of my window, what can I see?
I see pain and anger and people fighting.
Then it all stops - there was goodness, the fighting had gone.
People getting along.
I feel better now but it might not be long
The pain might start again and the goodness
Might go away!

**Connor Heys-Burke (8)**
**St Clement's CE Primary School, Higher Openshaw**

## When I Look Out My Window

When I look out my window, what do I see?
Birds and flowers and a big pretty tree.
But then I look around a little more
And what do I really see?
The flowers and birds, not for me.
Strangers and danger, that's important to see!

**Holly Cope (9)**
**St Clements CE Primary School, Higher Openshaw**

## Never Will We Part

Forever, ever on!
I want to be your friend
until death do us part.

I want to be your friend
when it snows in summer
and the sun shines in winter.

I want to be your friend
when the sun gets too hot.

We will be friends forever.
Never will we part!
*Never will we part!*

When the thunder comes down
that's when we will part.

**Ray-Leigh Birkett (9)**
**St Clement's CE Primary School, Higher Openshaw**

## The Life Of Friendship

Forever friends!

I want to be your friend
until the world blows up
and the sun crumbles.
Friendship forever.
Never will I part from you
until the time there are no trees
and the stars and space are gone.
Not till then will I part from you
But my spirit of friendship will always
be with you.

**Liam Quantrill (8)**
**St Clement's CE Primary School, Higher Openshaw**

## Growing Older

When I grow older, what will I be?
A mum or a dad or a buzzing bee?
A mum with children that look like trees?
A singer with lots of people throwing roses at me?
A pop star with children that love me?

When I grow older, what will I be?
A tiger that yawns or a lion that speaks?
A princess with a castle with a tap that leaks?
A zebra that has red rosy cheeks?

**Chloe Johnson (8)**
**St Clement's CE Primary School, Higher Openshaw**

## When I Grow Older

When I grow older what will I be?
A skilful footballer,
Scoring goals for everyone to see.
Everybody cheering for me.

When I grow older what will I be?
As rich as a king,
I will earn lots of money,
I will wear lots of bling.

**Jordan Pope (7)**
**St Clement's CE Primary School, Higher Openshaw**

## Road Safety

When I look out of my window, what can I see?
A world of horror that's what I can see.
People getting run over,
People breaking the speed limit.
People drink driving,
People not crossing as safely as can be.
This world is not safe for young children crossing the street.
I hate it for all these dangers - just be safe.

**Darren Ford (9)**
**St Clement's CE Primary School, Higher Openshaw**

## Darkness

Darkness is black and gooey like a pool of black slime.
Darkness tastes like dark black sour-tasting coal.
It smells like black smoke from a burning fire,
It feels like someone's wrapping a cloth around my face
So I can't see or breathe.
It reminds me of space without stars or planets.

**Greg Baylis (8)**
**St George's Central CE Primary School, Tyldesley**

## Anger

Anger is scarlet like an exploding volcano,
It sounds like fireworks and screamers.
It tastes like dribbling blood,
It smells like a dead animal.
It makes you go red in the face,
It feels like blood trickling down my arm.
It reminds me of flesh of a dead dinosaur.

**Jodie Broadbent (8)**
**St George's Central CE Primary School, Tyldesley**

## Fun

Fun is orange like a shining sun burning above your head.
Fun sounds like laughter and smiles on people's faces.
Fun tastes like happiness in the air.
Fun smells like every single person, bouncing up and down.
Fun looks like a crab achieving its goal.
Fun feels like getting a good thing.
Fun reminds me of my birthday, having *fun!*

**Lauren Clynch (9)**
**St George's Central CE Primary School, Tyldesley**

## Love

Love is a romantic, bright pink.
It sounds like robins whistling in the trees.
Love tastes really sweet like ice cream.
Love smells like blossoms in the trees.
Love looks like a couple that have just got married.
It feels like someone hugging you really tight.
It reminds me of having great and happy times.

This is love.

**Ellie Morgan Pace Derbyshire (8)**
**St George's Central CE Primary School, Tyldesley**

## Anger

Anger is red, like scarlet
It sounds like thunder and lightning in my head.
It tastes like sour lemons in my mouth.
It smells like dead fish in the sea.
It feels like a volcano erupting,
It looks like black in the sea.
It reminds me of punching a punch-bag.

That is anger.

**Katy Gerrard (9)**
**St George's Central CE Primary School, Tyldesley**

## The Feeling Of Love

This is the feeling of love,
It can show emotions
In our heads, the colour of pink
As well as dining music.

It tastes like the sweetest
Strawberry in your mouth
The picture of a love heart
It feels like you're being tickled.

It reminds me of a ballroom dance
With everyone's smiling face
Swirling, twirling in my tummy
A big smile on my face
That is love.

**Rosie Lummis (9)**
**St George's Central CE Primary School, Tyldesley**

## Fear

Fear is a polar bear, white like a glum shaking igloo.
It sounds like a gasping person shaking his head off.
It tastes bitter like a sour lollipop.
It smells like a werewolf's breath, breathing in your face.
It looks like someone is scared and in fear of something big.
It feels like freezing cold ice, dripping down your body.
It reminds me of a *monster,* trashing a city.
That is fear.

**Ryan Pownall (9)**
**St George's Central CE Primary School, Tyldesley**

## The Feeling Of Fear

Fear is a blood-red frightening colour
It looks and sounds like a monster
Screeching its long nails on a blackboard
In your mouth, it tastes like you are going to be sick
Also your knees go knobbly and feel like jelly
All this fear reminds me of my most terrible nightmare.

**Georgia Roberts (9)**
**St George's Central CE Primary School, Tyldesley**

## Fun

Fun is the colour of anger
It sounds like happiness being made
I have lots of fun, like sunlight being laid.

It tastes like something nice
It tastes to me of fruit
To people it smells like
Lovely cash or loot.

It looks like happy children
It feels like something soft
It reminds me of the first time
I skipped past the loft.

**Somer Shaw (8)**
**St George's Central CE Primary School, Tyldesley**

## Sadness

Sadness is violet like a swishing sea,
It sounds like the wind blowing in my ear until I go blue.
Sadness tastes like the salt in the sea.
It smells like smoke in the air.
It looks like my brother crying.
It feels like I'm dying.
It reminds me of being ill.

**Callum Shepherd (9)**
**St George's Central CE Primary School, Tyldesley**

## Darkness

Darkness is black like a quiet scary place,
It tastes like a cool breeze and it smells like food
Making me jealous.
It feels like a wooden floor moving,
It looks like black and a little bit of light.
It reminds me of a massive room
With no light in at all.

**Leah Evans (7)**
**St George's Central CE Primary School, Tyldesley**

## Love

Love smells like fun and laughter
People love you and people love me.
I blush in my cheeks.
'Why do people love?' my daughter asked me.
'I don't know? Do you?'
It looks like a love heart.
It sounds joyful,
It feels like someone is hugging you,
It tastes like popcorn.
It reminds me of me.

**Megan Jones (8)**
**St George's Central CE Primary School, Tyldesley**

## Love

Love is pink, like a rose
Love sounds like a bird singing.
Love tastes like a river.
Love smells like fun and laughter.
Love looks like a heart.
Love feels soft and warm.
Love reminds me of my baby cousin.

**Hayley Price (8)**
**St George's Central CE Primary School, Tyldesley**

## Love

Love is pink like a bunch of roses,
It tastes like a box of chocolates
Love smells like the sweetest rose perfume.
Love looks like a heart,
Love feels like a river flowing.
It reminds me of my cousin Beth.
That is love.

**Jessica Sloan (8)**
**St George's Central CE Primary School, Tyldesley**

## Love

Love is pink like a rainbow,
It sounds peaceful and quiet.
It tastes like a lovely piece of chocolate.
It smells like a beautiful rose.
It looks like a person being friendly to another person.
It feels happy like a church bell, ringing.
It reminds me of me and my sisters, never falling out.

**Ella Louise Warhurst (8)**
**St George's Central CE Primary School, Tyldesley**

## Love

Love is pink and red like someone's heart,
It sounds like someone sharing with someone else.
It tastes like a big colourful rainbow,
Love smells like beautiful flowers.
It looks like a big juicy rose,
Love feels like someone holding someone else's hand.
Love reminds me of all kinds of things.

**Lydia Megan Scales (8)**
**St George's Central CE Primary School, Tyldesley**

## Anger

Anger is like devils with sharp red horns
Anger is like a volcano, as hot as fire
Anger is like sharp prickly thorns
stabbing right through
Anger is like a mean liar
Anger is a crazy feeling
Anger needs to be changed to
happiness all over the world.

**Leah Pendlebury (10)**
**St George's Central CE Primary School, Tyldesley**

## Sadness

Sadness is like a rainy day,
Like a dark damp cave,
Like being as small as an ant,
Like being eaten by a monster (munch, munch!)
Like being in a world alone.
I never want to be sad again.

**Lauren Howarth (10)**
**St George's Central CE Primary School, Tyldesley**

## Happiness

Happiness is like . . . the midsummer breeze,
Wind flying round my hands and knees.
When I go to the countryside
I take a great big stride.

Bright red flowers,
I think I've got the powers.
When it is your birthday
Your wishes all come true.

**Heather Dunning (9)**
**St George's Central CE Primary School, Tyldesley**

# Never Fear Remember Joseph And Doris With Happiness

*(In memory of Joseph and Doris Williams, my great grandparents)*

Happiness is like receiving presents,
It's like a calm peaceful atmosphere all around you.
There is a rainbow of colours
There is a light blue sky,
And birds singing their sweet tune,
And everything is calm.

**Morgan Joseph Foster (10)**
**St George's Central CE Primary School, Tyldesley**

## Happiness

Happiness, like a spring dance
It puts you in a trance,
A rainbow of love comes down on you
The beaming sun has gone at last
What a wonderful sight of happiness.

*Cheep, cheep,* I hear the birdies sing,
A fantasy of tune.
The butterflies soar, hear them flutter.
A donkey snoring in the shade from the heat.
What a beautiful sound of happiness.

The whistle of the postman
The rustle of the trees, playing with the leaves.
A newborn baby,
Family, and friends are here with me.
I love the feeling of happiness.

**Bethany Paige Pavitt (10)**
**St George's Central CE Primary School, Tyldesley**

## Anger

Anger is like a volcano bursting everywhere,
It's like devils in Hell
And red and orange flames setting everything alight
And drums banging so hard, you can't hear anything.

Anger is like a room full of red lights,
And devil shadows creeping about
And is like two armies fighting with all bombs going off.
Then finally it will start to fade away.
The fight will *end!*

**Katie Louise Macafee (9)**
**St George's Central CE Primary School, Tyldesley**

## Anger

Anger is a rose colour; it's like an explosion,
It sounds like a dinosaur's dad calling for help.
It tastes like the worst thing you've ever tasted.

It smells like blood dripping down your legs, *ugh!*
It looks like a red devil showing your big fears.
It feels like the universe is cracking.
It reminds you of all of your scariest, biggest fears
that you've ever heard or seen.
I don't like anger; it can get you into a lot of trouble.

**Sam Borbash (7)**
**St George's Central CE Primary School, Tyldesley**

## Scared

Darkness is scary
My imagination runs riot
Thoughts of monsters fill my head
Dark angry faces glare at me out of the shadows
And stop me sleeping.

**Corey Roberts (9)**
**St George's Central CE Primary School, Tyldesley**

## Frustration

Frustration is like a game
A volcano waiting to erupt
Breaking stuff around the house
Going as red as blood
It is like pulling your hair out.

**Josef Hampson (10)**
**St George's Central CE Primary School, Tyldesley**

## Happiness

Happiness is like getting a new pet to look after
Happiness is like winning a prize
Happiness is like Christmas Day
Happiness is like Easter time
Happiness is like your birthday
When your wishes come true.
You will see flowers in the daylight
In the countryside.

**Lauren Toone (10)**
**St George's Central CE Primary School, Tyldesley**

## Happiness

Happiness is like flowers in the long green grass,
Happiness is like when you go to the countryside and see lots of trees.
Happiness is like butterflies flying all around you in the breeze.
Happiness is like when you win something really special.
Happiness is like when you go away on holiday.
Happiness is like a rainbow of colours.

**Leah Statham (10)**
**St George's Central CE Primary School, Tyldesley**

## Fun!

You have a laugh with your friends,
plus it never ends.

Fun is like a ball of laughing gas,
that is what fun is.

Fun is like playing outside and
fun is going on a roller coaster ride.

Now my friends have fun with me,
now I'm going in for a cup of tea.

Everybody has had fun and at the end of the day,
it's time for fun to go away.

**Luke Hudson (11)**
**St George's Central CE Primary School, Tyldesley**

## Love

Love is just like melted chocolate,
dropping on a sponge cake.
It sounds like diamonds dropping
from the blue sea clouds.

Love is all about a girl and a boy
getting together,
They feel excited and
warm inside.

**Veronika Jelisejeva (11)**
**St George's Central CE Primary School, Tyldesley**

# Love!

Love is like a flying bird
It whistles upon us
Love smells perfectly sweet
It feels like a bright red rose
Love is like a robin whilst it sings a happy song
It never lets you down
Love decorates your heart with laughter
Love is the perfect roller coaster!

**Beth Sutherland (10)**
**St George's Central CE Primary School, Tyldesley**

## Love

Love can be good
Love can be bad
You love your mum
You love your dad

You need love to smile
You even need love to frown
Love goes that extra mile.

**Robert Mann (11)**
**St George's Central CE Primary School, Tyldesley**

## Nervous

Nervous is a bad kind of disease,
When you're nervous you shake in your shoes.

It feels like your head is closing in,
Your world feels like it's shrinking quickly.

Your heart pounds really violently
The smell is of a horrible musk.

Your mouth has a bitter taste of waste,
Being nervous is a hard thing to cope.

Butterflies will come if you're nervous,
Nervous is shyness but a lot worse.

**Alex Bell (10)**
**St George's Central CE Primary School, Tyldesley**

## Love

Love is like melted chocolate
Drizzling on a caramel sponge cake
It sounds like magic gems dropping
And it's in the friends you make.

Love always tastes yummy
Like a treasure trove full of treats
It feels like lovely petals
And in the friends you meet.

Love is something special
Between a girl and boy
Love is a big red heart
It's a cup full of joy.

**Lauren Aspinall (11)**
**St George's Central CE Primary School, Tyldesley**

## Anger

A powerful rush
A hot push

A red flame
That cannot be tamed

An uncontrollable force
A heat source

An everlasting burst
You feel like you're cursed

A bubbling fear
A hot tear

*Anger.*

**Luke Unsworth (10)**
**St George's Central CE Primary School, Tyldesley**

## Fun

Fun is like a burst of laughter
Fun is like running a bit faster.

Fun is at a party
Playing with your best friend Marty.

It tastes like an ice cream sundae
It's like being at a beach on a Monday.

Fun is always everywhere,
Especially when you are there.

**Bradley Evans (10)**
**St George's Central CE Primary School, Tyldesley**

## Fear And Anger

Fear is a cold-blooded hound
that eats at you every time you
hear a scary sound.

Anger is a ball of fire
that burns and burns
like my heart's desire.

A powerful rush
a burning bush,
A ball of fire
my heart's desire.

Anger is a volcano
that explodes
when you lose a game.

Fear is a fog that's
misty and hisses
passing the log.

**David Borbash (11)**
**St George's Central CE Primary School, Tyldesley**

## Love

*Love* is like biting into a
strawberry and tastes like
a drink of cherry.
It feels like a bright red rose
and sometimes gets thrown back
at your nose!

Sometimes love is about fun and laughter,
then you regret it the day after.
A powerful blush
A big green bush!

**Ryan Little (10)**
**St George's Central CE Primary School, Tyldesley**

## Anger

Anger is like a volcano
bubbling inside,
When it erupts
it feels like it's died.

It tastes like vindaloo
that burns like fire,
It's like a virus
and cuts like barbed wire.

**Brandon Roche (11)**
**St George's Central CE Primary School, Tyldesley**

## Poem Of Love

Love is so special
Love is in the air.
Where could love strike next?
My mum says, 'Anywhere!'

Love is a sigh of happiness
Lots of laughter and joy,
Especially on Valentine's Day
A love between a girl or boy.

Love is like melted chocolate
And smells like a scented rose
So let's get on together
With the man or woman you chose.

**Rachael Molyneaux (10)**
**St George's Central CE Primary School, Tyldesley**

## Different Feelings

Love is like a round ball, it's warm inside
Anger is like a strong wave.
Madness is like a roaring tiger,
Happiness is a flying butterfly.

When you are happy
You feel like you're on top of the world.
It's like a wave crashing on the sea,
High and banging, you can't even see.

**Ebonni Yates (10)**
**St George's Central CE Primary School, Tyldesley**

## Love

Love is pink and red,
Love is sweet and shining.
Love feels special and happy,
Love tastes like sweets.
Love smells like flowers,
Love sounds like violins and the harmonica.
Love looks like flowers and hearts.
Love reminds me of chocolate, hearts and flowers.

So remember love to be happy.

**Scarlett Braisdell (9)**
**St George's Central CE Primary School, Tyldesley**

## Hate

Hate is black as smoke, like a stormy night sky,
It sounds like blood-curdling thunder and lightning.
You can taste red blood,
The horrid stench of rotting corpses with black flies flying around.
It looks like many things, mostly dark.
It reminds me of horrid nightmares.
You can feel horrible fire in your hands.
This is hate.

**Scott Cummings (9)**
**St George's Central CE Primary School, Tyldesley**

## Sadness

Sadness is sky-blue, it is like a down, sad face,
It sounds like someone is dying and his blood is pouring out.
It smells like onions, which make me cry.
It looks like my dad dying.
It feels like I am going in a devil's pot.
It does remind me of my brother dying.
I am really sad and it is not in my dreams.

**Kyle Stirling (8)**
**St George's Central CE Primary School, Tyldesley**

## Love

Love is an amazing pink that fills the air,
It sounds like someone having a great time.
Love tastes like sweets and chocolate.
It smells like blossom growing on the tree.
It looks like a happy couple.
Love feels like people hugging you.
Love reminds me about people that
Have happiness inside them.

**Lena Jane Welsh (9)**
**St George's Central CE Primary School, Tyldesley**

## Happiness Is When . . .

A rainbow of colours are showering over you,
You're in your own magical fantasy,
All you dreams and wishes are coming true,
Sunshine with glowing rays, flooding you with love.

Everybody smiles at you,
Birds sing lovely chirpy songs.
The tune of the milkman's whistle
A new door has been opened for you,
Opened wide.

You are joyful and hopeful
Inside you're filling with faith.
You believe you are the best
And overcome your fear.

You're full of love and hope,
You're feeling happy and carefree.
Everything affects the way you feel,
You feel, you feel, you feel.

Spread your wings,
Fly out in the sky.
Do everything you've always wanted,
Without a worry or care.

You feel sparkly and shiny,
You feel new and excited,
You feel calm and restful,
You feel great and joyful.

When your mum cooks your favourite meals,
Making new friends.
Lots of praise and a smiley face
When you're proud and confident in what you do.

Inside you're jumping for joy,
You can't wait for what comes next,
You're having the time of your life,
Because you are *happy!*

**Alice Lummis-Green (10)**
**St George's Central CE Primary School, Tyldesley**

## Puzzled

Puzzled, puzzled, puzzled,
Puzzled is when you don't know what to do,
Puzzled, puzzled, puzzled,
Puzzled when a horse goes moo!

Puzzled, puzzled, puzzled,
Puzzled is when you scratch your head,
Puzzled, puzzled, puzzled,
Puzzled when you don't know what you've said!

**Sam Champion (10)**
**St George's Central CE Primary School, Tyldesley**

## Heartbroken

When someone is heartbroken, they act very sad,
Heartbroken, heartbroken, where do you go?
Heartbroken, heartbroken, what do you do?
Heartbroken, is like a hole in your heart.
A sword plunged through your heart
With blood spilling out!

**Carenza Reece (9)**
**St George's Central CE Primary School, Tyldesley**

## Love

Love is kind and caring
It sounds like birds tweeting and singing a song.
It tastes like a rainbow
It smells like a flower
It feels like a rose
It looks like a bird flying in the sky
It reminds me of Blackpool.

**Lewis Crowther (7)**
**St George's Central CE Primary School, Tyldesley**

## The Writer Of This Poem

*(Based on 'The Writer of this Poem' by Roger McGough)*

The writer of this poem
Is bigger than a house
As heavy as a tree trunk
As tiny as a mouse

As deadly as a shark
As momentous as a dinosaur
As sleepy as my sister
As scary as a roar

As moody as a monster
As soft as a pillow
As cunning as a fox
As tall as a willow

As furry as a wolf
As silly as a clown
As muddy as a caveman
As sad as a frown.

**Hugh Nicholas Wright (8)**
**St Mary's CE Primary School, Urmston**

## Life Is . . .

Life is a show at the theatre
Life is sunburn at the beach
Life is a Chinese on a Friday night
Life is a bully at school
Life is a treat on your birthday
Life is a punch by your brother or sister
Life is an ice cream in your back garden
Life is as bad as a cold in winter.

**Sophie Phillips (9)**
**St Mary's CE Primary School, Urmston**

## The Writer Of This Poem

*(Based on 'The Writer of this Poem' by Roger McGough)*

The writer of this poem
Is as smelly as Paul
As big as a skyscraper
As good as a mall.

As cool as a dude
As scary as a lion
As much fun as a circus
As hot as an iron.

As stupid as can be
As fast as a car
As scary as a monster
He makes you say *argh!*

**Warren Noon (8)**
**St Mary's CE Primary School, Urmston**

## The Writer Of This Poem

*(Based on 'The Writer of this Poem' by Roger McGough)*

The writer of this poem
Is as fat as a ball
As smelly as a shoe
As big as a hall

As comfy as a blanket
As yellow as a cat
As thin as a pin
As cosy as a bobble hat

As friendly as a friend
As basic as a cube
As scary as a beast
As disgusting as a Choob

As cute as a dog
As furry as a coat
As flexible as Homer Simpson
As cold as a boat

As weird as fake hair
As useful as a rubber
As ugly as a monster
As tasty as Huba-Buba.

**Lewis Wright (8)**
**St Mary's CE Primary School, Urmston**

## Life Is . . .

Life is an ice cream on the soft sand,
Life is going on a holiday,
Life is buying sweets.
Life is having fun on my bike,
Life is playing with your mates.
Life is going out for tea and with your family,
Life is tidying up and being patient.
Life is getting dressed to go to a party.

**Olivia Murphy (9)**
**St Mary's CE Primary School, Urmston**

## The Writer Of This Poem

*(Based on 'The Writer of this Poem' by Roger McGough)*

The writer of this poem
Is as wet as a pond
As long as a snake
As magic as a wand

As funny as a clown
As still as a pencil case
As sharp as a frown
As beautiful as a face

As sleepy as a mole
As gooey as glue
As big as a hole
As scary as a pirate's crew

As cool as a cat
As mad as a moose
As flat as a mat
As creepy as a goose.

**Charlotte Jones (9)**
**St Mary's CE Primary School, Urmston**

## Dog - Haiku

Me and my dog Sam
We're happily playing with
A blue and red ball.

**Hannah Yates (9)**
**St Mary's CE Primary School, Urmston**

## Life Is . . .

Life is a chocolate bar melting in the sun
Life is sunburn on the beach
Life is an Easter egg
Life is like a cut finger
Life is a kiss on the cheek
Life is a hotpot around the fire
Life is a warm cappuccino
Life is a pizza on a Friday night.

**Nial Edwards (8)**
**St Mary's CE Primary School, Urmston**

## The Writer Of This Poem

*(Based on 'The Writer of this Poem' by Roger McGough)*

The writer of this poem
Is as moody as a cow
As furry as a bear
As muddy as a sow

As soft as a chair
As sad as a clown
As sleepy as a bat
As snuggly as my dressing gown

As small as a hat
As dumb as a duck
As wriggly as a rat
As big as a book.

**Chloe Woods (9)**
**St Mary's CE Primary School, Urmston**

## Me

I love to dance, sing too.
I like drawing pictures, do you?
I like collecting all sorts of rings,
And I like lending things!

I like cleaning so much,
Someone's given me that special touch.
I don't like singing to a crowd
But I still sing out *loud!*

Every day I have a smile
For a very long while!
I like giving a helping hand.
One day I wish to be in a band!

**Shai Burke (8)**
**St Wilfrid's CE Primary School, Northenden**

## Wrestling

W WE stands for World Wrestling Entertainment
R oyal rumble is when all the wrestlers come together
and fight each other.
E very wrestler fights,
S ometimes wrestlers bleed
T here are different belts you have to earn. The belts,
like Batista who won the heavyweight.
L esnar is a wrestler.
I like wrestling, but my mum doesn't.
N ever try to fight a wrestler.
G o and see a match, you'll have to pay a lot.

**Jereem Kunnassety (9)**
**St Wilfrid's CE Primary School, Northenden**

## Lynx

Lynx leaping on the mountain
Chasing deer all day
Roaring at the puma, protecting her prey

Lynx live in caves on mountains
Looking after her cubs
At two months old they wander out of the cave
To see the world.

**Emily Greenwood (8)**
**St Wilfrid's CE Primary School, Northenden**

## Smith

S mith is a top player
M an Utd are the best
I like him a lot
T hey are at the top of the League
H e plays for Man Utd.

**Jordan Lee (9)**
**St Wilfrid's CE Primary School, Northenden**

## My Family

My sister is mean
She's as mean as can be
She shouts, she screams
She hurts me

My mum is loving
She's as loving as can be
She's kind, she's nice
She hugs me

My brothers are horrid
They're as horrid as can be
They scream, they shout
They hate me.

**Caitlin McNiven (8)**
**St Wilfrid's CE Primary School, Northenden**

## Kittens In The Garden

Kittens in the garden
Lying in the sun
Come on kittens
Let's go and have some fun!

Kittens in the house
Running up and down the stairs
Getting up to mischief
They think the house is theirs.

Kittens at the funfair
Playing on the slide
Come on kittens
Shall we go on a different ride?

**Charlotte Fitzgerald (9)**
**St Wilfrid's CE Primary School, Northenden**

## The Sadness Of Death

Sadness is like a white desperate family
looking for someone to be by their side.
It sounds like the crying of a mother
with no one there for her.
It tastes like the boy who had no parents
around him.
It smells like the droplets of water being crushed
as they fall sadly on to the floor.
It looks like a child being beaten up by everyone
in his family.
It feels like the sadness of a baby dying.
It reminds me of the beating of a child gasping for breath.

**Aqib Hanif (9)**
**St Wilfrid's CE Primary School, Northenden**

## Laughter

Laugher is pink that makes the boys wink,
It sounds like water that's dropping in the sink.
It tastes like oranges that make me think.
It smells like onions that make me blink.
It looks like juice that you really want to drink.
It feels like someone starting to shrink,
It reminds of the colour pink.

**Choni Kenny (9)**
**St Wilfrid's CE Primary School, Northenden**

## Darkness

Darkness is black, like a black hole sucking you inside it,
It sounds like your hair is an army of nits.
It tastes like bitter salt and road grit,
It smells like sweating armpits.
It looks like you're in a huge dusty pit,
It feels like you've been punched and hit.
It reminds me of the dark winter nights.

**Joshua Ashman (10)**
**St Wilfrid's CE Primary School, Northenden**

## Anger

Anger is red like a volcano about to explode,
Anger sounds like a little man stamping around in my head.
It tastes like the salty seawater.
It smells like steam in the bathroom after you've had a shower.
It feels hot and it reminds me of fire.

**Ellie Forden (10)**
**St Wilfrid's CE Primary School, Northenden**

## The Exploding Caravan

Hate is red like an exploding caravan in the burning sun,
It sounds like a bomb exploding in my brain.
It tastes like a red-hot chilli pepper
But I won't taste it anyway!
It smells like pieces of rotten cheese.
It looks like a thousand fireworks going off at once.
It feels like a bun being burnt.
It reminds me of the planet Mars exploding.

**Jacob Matthew Redman (9)**
**St Wilfrid's CE Primary School, Northenden**

## Anger Is Red!

Anger is red like a roaring hot fire,
It sounds like a fighting tiger that roars.
It tastes like horrible burnt firewood,
It smells like toast that has been burned.
It looks like people dancing round and round,
It feels like I am melting away.
It reminds me of being with my family.

**Tilly Clarke (9)**
**St Wilfrid's CE Primary School, Northenden**

## The Flames Of Anger

Anger is red like an aggressive fire
destroying everything in its path.
It sounds like people in pain
doing things uncontrollably.
It tastes like fiery peppers
burning your mouth.
It looks like a fire trying
to take you in.
It smells like smoke and
it makes you choke.
It feels like you're melting
in a bad dream.
It reminds me of chaos
and destruction.

**Rommel Burke (9)**
**St Wilfrid's CE Primary School, Northenden**

## Happiness

Happiness is multicoloured like a
bright rainbow in the sky.
It sounds like tiny singing birds
flying by.
It tastes like hot sweet apple pie.
It smells like roses that are ready
to buy.
It looks like a big beautiful butterfly.
It feels like you're on top of a mountain
very, very high.
It reminds me of my mum relaxing
on the sofa, there she lies.

**Chloe Bottrell (10)**
**St Wilfrid's CE Primary School, Northenden**

## Fun, Fun, Fun

Fun is green like the lovely grass,
It sounds like a waterfall trickling down
the bumpy rocks into the river of joy.
It tastes sweet, sweeter than sugar
the sweetest thing ever.
It smells like a rose in its full bloom.
It looks like a group of children playing,
It feels very joyful and merry.
It reminds me of my friends.

**Gareth Wilson (10)**
**St Wilfrid's CE Primary School, Northenden**

## Fear

Fear is black like a dark room in a haunted house
and watching you, the eyes of a frightful bogeyman.
It sounds like a thousand rats squeaking as they
rush round and round.
Dust blowing in my face and mouth, but it tastes
like flesh and bone.
It smells like a billion rotting dead things in smelly sewage.
It looks like my great grandmother's attic and more scary.
It feels like I'm alone, but I'm not.
It reminds me of the black hole sucking out my courage.
When I look, lava surrounds me, so I can't get out.

**David Smith (9)**
**St Wilfrid's CE Primary School, Northenden**

## Dark Shadow

Darkness is black, like a dark shadow, standing in the room.
It sounds like a thump and creaking from behind.
It tastes like human sweat and spiders and blood.
It smells like burning toast on fire and something
that makes you sick like a stink bomb.
It looks like a nightmare and a dark shadow
standing in the dark, watching every move you make.
It feels like cold, filling your body and so lonely
and you just want to get out of it.
It reminds me of when I was five, something
terrible happened.

**Curtis Gallagher (10)**
**St Wilfrid's CE Primary School, Northenden**

## Fun, Fun, Fun

Fun, fun, fun is orange like the sun,
It sounds like laughter and children having fun.
It tastes like a rose and smells like one too.
It looks like people having fun.
It reminds me of having a fun time.

**Jamie Gibson (9)**
**St Wilfrid's CE Primary School, Northenden**

## Laughter

Laughter is a green feather that tickles you
to make you laugh.
It sounds like a fly splattering on the wall.
It tastes like a smelly sock.
It smells like a rotten egg.
It looks like a green bogey tickling you
and making you cry.
It feels like love and laughter all over your body.
It reminds me of what witches make.

**Alexandra Jane Heathcote (9)**
**St Wilfrid's CE Primary School, Northenden**

## So Much Fun At The Party

Fun is blue, like the bright, breezy cool sky,
It sounds like the children having a party, that's fun.
It tastes like a luscious big fruit pie.
It smells like yummy sugar Haribos on a plain bun.
It looks like the children enjoy this film very much.
It feels like they are feeling warm, such and such.
It reminds me of my friends' sleepover party.

**Lucy To (10)**
**St Wilfrid's CE Primary School, Northenden**

## Sweet Laughing

Laughter is pink, like a loud, happy joyful noise,
It sounds like having fun, which is very good.
It tastes sweet, sweet as honey.
It smells like roses, fresh roses ever.
It looks like joy, joyful than I had.
It feels like fun, best thing ever.
It reminds me of having lots of fun.

**Carmen Chu (10)**
**St Wilfrid's CE Primary School, Northenden**

## Dislike

Hate is red like the deadly blood of a person,
It feels like a cold-hearted soul with hate.
Hate sounds like kids shouting at each other.
It smells like a disgusting old fire, burning.
It tastes like a piece of coal that is burning away.
It looks like an angry gorilla.
It reminds me of my aunty Betty.

**Sam Grant (10)**
**St Wilfrid's CE Primary School, Northenden**

## Sadness

Sadness is blue like the beautiful blue sky,
It sounds like a drum going faster and faster
down your ears.
It tastes like a pool of tears roaring
around your eyes.
It smells like a muddy puddle running
down the stream.
It looks like a river of tears going past you.
It feels like a trail of mud going down
the street.
It reminds me of the fair, all gooey and yucky.

**Zoe Norton (9)**
**St Wilfrid's CE Primary School, Northenden**

## The Silence Of The Cloud

Silence is white, like a cloud in the sky,
It sounds like the rain patting down from the sky,
It tastes like snow melting in your mouth.
It smells like the summer is going to pop out.
It looks like no one is going to come out.
I feel a bit lonely, but that is all right.
It reminds me of my grandma when she was alive.

**Rachel Ashcroft (10)**
**St Wilfrid's CE Primary School, Northenden**

## Stress Head

Anger is red like a bunch of red roses, freshly picked,
It sounds like a drum being banged on my head.
It tastes like an ice lolly that has just been licked,
It smells like burning toast when you are lying in bed.
It looks like a giant, stamping around,
It feels like I'm alone but somehow I'm not.
It reminds me of a big muddy mound.

**Faye Ashworth (9)**
**St Wilfrid's CE Primary School, Northenden**

## Darkness

Darkness is black like you're locked in a room with no light,
It sounds like a scary ghost in the night.
It tastes like eating spiders in broad daylight.
It smells like green grunge that gives you a fright.
It looks like a giant that's going to give you a bite.
It feels like an ant nibbling your toes.
It reminds me of a wolf in the full moon.

**Sally Robertson (9)**
**St Wilfrid's CE Primary School, Northenden**

## Heart

Love is red, red like your heart
It sounds like you're afraid.
Afraid of what?
The one thing I want to taste is your heart,
I smell it every day.
When I get a response, it's a beautiful
gleaming smile.
It looks like love, love to me and
it feels like it too, you're the one for me.
It reminds me of my mum and dad
the ones that look after me.

**Lizzie Marvin (10)**
**St Wilfrid's CE Primary School, Northenden**

## Hate Is Horrible And Silly

Hate is red like the colour of blood when you scrape your leg,
It sounds like a big bomb exploding in my head.
It tastes like dirt when it is all dry and hard.
It smells like a newly opened birthday card.
It looks like a monster lurking in the dark.
It feels like a piece of rough tree bark,
It reminds me of when I was a little boy,
I wanted to kill a friend, when he broke my new favourite toy.

**James Christian Brownhill (9)**
**St Wilfrid's CE Primary School, Northenden**

## The Darkness

Darkness is black like a scary dark night,
Be careful or you might get a fright.
It sounds like the drip, drip of a tap,
It tastes like a horrible dark chocolate bar.
It smells like a fire that has just been lit.
It looks like a shadow in a dark room.
It feels like someone is following you,
It reminds of a film called 'The Ring'.

**Lauren Cassidy (9)**
**St Wilfrid's CE Primary School, Northenden**

## Fun

Fun is green like gorgeous grass in the glistening sun,
It sounds like sunshine.
It tastes like a wibbly-wobbly lime jelly.
It smells like a mango.
It looks like the green shell of a gorgeous mango.
It feels like the hairy shell of a coconut.
It reminds me of the planet Venus.
I love the colour green, it is my favourite colour.
It is such fun, I think I'll do it again.

**Rebecca Stapley (9)**
**St Wilfrid's CE Primary School, Northenden**

## Darkness Is Creepy

Darkness is like a black cloud falling from the sky.
It sounds like a creepy gate banging.
It tastes like a sandwich left under my bed for six years.
It smells like a smelly hairy armpit.
It looks like a dark scary man chasing me.
It feels like something crushing your soul.
It reminds me of a black leopard ripping me, bit by bit.

**Kyle Harte (10)**
**St Wilfrid's CE Primary School, Northenden**

## Fear

Fear is dark like a black hole sucking up all my
courage and bravery,
It sounds like a deserted town and all you can hear
is the wind.
It tastes like food that's a thousand years old.
It smells like dead rats and a sewage pipe, mixed together.
It looks like a sly fox getting ready to pounce on its prey.
It feels like someone is watching me.
It reminds me of a werewolf in the shadows.

**Jack Waters (9)**
**St Wilfrid's CE Primary School, Northenden**

## As Silent As Mice

Silence is white, white like the cool relaxing moon
that makes the dark so bright.
Silence doesn't look like much at all because
it's a place in your head where no one can get to.
You can ride a green scaly dragon,
Go under a waterfall or in the cosy patch
on a giddy kangaroo!
Silence is very quiet indeed,
it sounds like a ladybird walking or a
dog taking little nibbles at his lead.
Silence tastes like chocolate melting in your mouth,
chocolates from the finest chocolates down south.

**Cameron David Pilling (9)**
**St Wilfrid's CE Primary School, Northenden**

# Young Writers Information

We hope you have enjoyed reading this book - and that you will continue to enjoy it in the coming years.

If you like reading and writing poetry drop us a line, or give us a call, and we'll send you a free information pack.

Alternatively if you would like to order further copies of this book or any of our other titles, then please give us a call or log onto our website at www.youngwriters.co.uk

**Young Writers Information**
**Remus House**
**Coltsfoot Drive**
**Peterborough**
**PE2 9JX**

**(01733) 890066**